# What I Wish for

# 1

**I wish I could give you a**

________________________________________.

# 2

I wish the world knew about your

________________________________________.

# 3

I wish we could

________________________________________

together one day.

# 4

I wish I were as good as you at

________________________________________.

# 5

I wish I had known you when

________________________________________.

# 6

You are my favorite

________________________________________

in the world.

# 7

I wish more people could

________________________________________

your

________________________________________.

# 8

I wish you'd start

________________________________________ .

9

I wish you'd stop

____________________________________________________________ .

# 10

I wish I could bottle and sell your

_______________________________________________ .

# 11

If you were a city, you'd be

______________________________________________.

# 12

I wish you knew how much I

______________________________

you.

# 13

I wish we could play

_______________________________________________

every

_______________________________________________.

# 14

I wish we could go

---

again.

# 15

I wish the world had more of your unique

________________________________________ .

# 16

I hope you get to

________________________________________

someday.

# 17

I wish your

appreciated how

you are.

# 18

I wish we were

________________________________________

right now.

19

I wish you'd show me how to

________________________________________.

# 20

I believe we'd make a great

________________________________________

team.

# 21

I wish you were flying to

________________________________________

tonight.

# 22

I wish you weren't always right about

________________________________________.

23

It would make me happy if you could

______________________________________________

whenever you wanted.

# 24

I wish I knew your secret for

________________________________________.

25

I wish I could make your

________________________________________

go away.

# 26

I wish someone would

________________________________

a

________________________________

about you.

# 27

Sometimes, I wish you'd never have to

______________________________________________

again.

28

It's fun to

________________________________________

with you.

# 29

I wish we were still

________________________________________________ .

# 30

You deserve the

________________________________________

award.

# 31

I wish you'd let me

________________________________________

for you.

32

I wish your

______________________________________

could be studied by science.

# 33

I wish you weren't so good at giving me

______________________________________________.

34

If you were a drink, you'd be

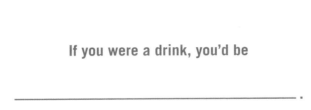

______________________________________________.

35

I wish I had your taste in

________________________________________ .

# 36

I wish I could buy you that

________________________________________

you want.

# 37

I hope you get to

________________________________

your favorite

________________________________

soon.

# 38

I’d rather

________________________________________

with you than anyone else.

# 39

I wish I could get you

right now.

40

I hope you never forget that I

______________________________________________ .

# 41

If I could grant you one wish it'd be

________________________________________.

42

I wish everybody were as

________________________________________

as you.

# 43

If you were an instrument, you'd be

______________________________________________.

44

I wish I had your

____________________________________________.

45

I wish you weren't so darn

______________________________________________.

# 46

I hope to see you

one day.

# 47

I wish you'd feel free to

________________________________________

more often.

# 48

It's hard to put into words how much I wish

______________________________________.

# 49

I hope our

________________________________________

lasts forever.

50

I wish you all the

________________________________________

on the planet.

I Wish You
All Good Things.

Created and published by Knock Knock
Distributed by Who's There Inc.
Venice, CA 90291
**knockknockstuff.com**


Made in China



**UPC**: 825703-50064-6 **ISBN**: 978-160106564-3
10 9 8 7